This book belongs to:

....

....

Bright Sparks books have been created
with the help of experts in early childhood education.
They are designed to help young children achieve
success in their early learning years.

Retold by Sue Graves
Illustrated by Adrienne Salgado

Reading consultants: Betty Root and Monica Hughes

This is a Parragon Publishing book
First published 2006

Parragon Publishing
Queen Street House
4 Queen Street
Bath BA1 1HE, UK

Copyright © Parragon Books Ltd 2006

ISBN 1-40547-962-0
Printed in China

Little Red
Riding Hood

p

Helping your child read

Bright Sparks readers are closely linked to recognized learning strategies. Their vocabulary has been carefully selected from word lists recommended by educational experts.

Read the story

Read the story
to your child
a few times.

Little Red Riding Hood saw some
flowers in the woods.
"I will pick some flowers for
Granny," she said.
Little Red Riding Hood stopped to
pick the flowers.
Then she met a wolf.

12

Follow your finger

Run your finger under
the text as you read.
Soon your child will begin to
follow the words with you.

Look at the pictures
Talk about the pictures. They will
help your child understand the story.

She met a wolf.

13

Give it a try
Let your child try
reading the large
type on each
right-hand page.
It repeats a line
from the story.

Join in
When your child is ready,
encourage him or her to join in with
the main story text. Shared reading
is the first step to reading alone.

7

Once there was a little girl called
Little Red Riding Hood.

One day her mother said,
"Granny is ill.
Please go and see her.
You can take her this basket of fruit."

Little Red Riding Hood.

Granny lived in a house in the woods.
So Little Red Riding Hood took the
basket of fruit, and she went into
the woods to see her granny.

She went into the woods to
see her granny.

Little Red Riding Hood saw some
flowers in the woods.
"I will pick some flowers for
Granny," she said.
Little Red Riding Hood stopped to
pick the flowers.
Then she met a wolf.

She met a wolf.

The wolf was hungry.
He wanted to eat Little Red
Riding Hood.
"What are you doing in the
woods?" he said sweetly.
Little Red Riding Hood said,
"I'm going to see my granny.
She lives in a house in the woods."

"I'm going to see my granny."

The bad wolf said to himself, "I will go to Granny's house and eat her."
So the wolf ran to Granny's house.

When the wolf got to Granny's house, he ate her in one gulp.
The wolf put on Granny's clothes and got into her bed.

The wolf put on Granny's clothes.

Little Red Riding Hood got to
Granny's house.
She knocked on the door.
"Come in, come in," said the wolf.
"Hello!" said Little Red Riding Hood.

"Hello!" said Little
Red Riding Hood.

Little Red Riding Hood went up to
the bed.
"What big eyes you have!" she said.
So the wolf said sweetly,
"All the better to see you with."
"But what big ears you have!" she said.
So the wolf said very sweetly,
"All the better to hear you with!"

"What big eyes you have!"

Then Little Red Riding Hood said,
"Yes, but what big teeth you have!"
And the wolf said very, very sweetly,
"All the better to eat you with."

And then the wolf jumped out of bed.

"What big teeth you have!"

"I'm going to eat you!" said the wolf.
So Little Red Riding Hood cried,
"Help! Help!"
But the wolf ate her in one gulp.

"I'm going to eat you!" said
the wolf.

A woodcutter was in the woods.
He heard Little Red Riding Hood.
So the woodcutter ran to help.

The woodcutter killed the wolf.
He cut the wolf open.
Granny and Little Red Riding Hood
jumped out.
They were very happy.

Granny and Little Red Riding
Hood jumped out.

Look back in your book.
Can you read these words?

Granny

wolf

basket

house

bed

flowers

Can you answer these questions?

Where did
Granny live?

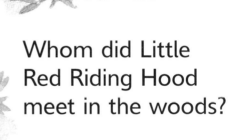

Whom did Little
Red Riding Hood
meet in the woods?

Who killed the wolf?

The End